Skills for writing
Contents

CW00351538

Teachers' notes

Introduction

The activities in this book are devised to help children within years 3–6 who are having difficulties with their spelling and writing.

The tasks meet the requirements of Attainment Target 3 in the National Curriculum for English, Levels 1, 2 and working towards 3. The activity sheets are divided into four sections, covering handwriting, spelling, grammar and creative or free writing. To gain maximum benefit from these pages the sheets should be incorporated into a learning environment, covering all areas of English; talking, listening, thinking, reading and writing. Used in isolation the sheets could be seen by the children as just a time-filling activity. It is important to use them as part of a purposeful exercise, so that the task is meaningful and valued.

Children with writing difficulties do need plenty of opportunities to reinforce the skills practised on these sheets, which can serve as models for further similar activities.

Aims of this book

The aims of this book are:
• to help children understand the importance of correct formation of the letters linked to letter patterns;
• to extend spelling patterns using joined up handwriting;
• to help children to become proficient and accurate spellers using both visual and auditory approaches;
• to introduce simple grammatical terms and skills;
• to understand the fundamentals of sentence structure and basic punctuation;
• to offer examples of different forms of writing and provide practice using a variety of texts.

Notes on individual activities

Handwriting

These worksheets help children understand the principles involved in learning and reinforcing joined up handwriting. By giving examples of a group of letters combined with a handwriting pattern, it is hoped that children with poor motor control or incorrect letter formation can be given confidence by practising these combinations. Encourage the children to practise these patterns in borders or design work. Remind them of the letter families.

Children should not think that handwriting is an easy option. Good handwriting is something that requires hard work and when successful is something of which they can be very proud.

Handwriting check-list

• Pencil grip: hold fingers not too close to the point of the pencil. Suggest a triangular pencil to help a poor grip.
• Sitting position: both feet should be on the floor, the forearm should be on the table. Use the non-writing hand to hold the paper steady.
• Paper: using guidelines, wider lined paper, or writing on every other line are all helpful alternatives to try, as necessary.
• Left handers: provide a higher chair which can help children to see over the top of their work. If you are demonstrating to the children, use your left hand. Ensure they have enough space to work.

Pages 5–8: Handwriting 1–4

Explain to the children the reason for linking the writing patterns to their letter families. Once the children have mastered the patterns, the correct formation of the letters can follow. Encourage the children to practise the patterns on separate sheets of paper; they may find it easier to practise the patterns in a larger sized handwriting.

The patterns and letter families are introduced in four activity sheets. Not all the letters belong to a letter family and some letters could fit into more than one family. Check this against your own school handwriting policy. Many teachers also feel strongly about the formation of some letters such as k or k, f or f. Adapt these activity sheets if necessary.

Page 9: Handwriting 5

This activity sheet covers some 'tricky bits' in handwriting. Encourage the children to analyse their own handwriting and work out the parts that they particularly find 'tricky'. This could be an extension activity of value to the individual. Make sure all children are familiar with the terms 'descender' and 'ascender' before they begin this sheet.

Spelling

To become confident and competent spellers children need to be able to link letter sounds with spelling patterns. They need to recognise how a word looks as well as how it sounds, so both visual and auditory skills need to be developed. In this visual age of the computer, television and video, children tend not to pay so much attention to auditory stimulus. They need to be taught how the written words and sounds correspond.

Recent research suggests that children develop the ability to hear individual sounds in words, later than once was thought. Initially children become aware of syllables within words, recognising onset (the first sound) and rime (the remainder of the syllable). Once children are able to recognise rhyme, they can be taught to make analogies with words. This means they can spell several words based on one letter sequence.

Never let children think they are poor spellers. A positive approach to good attempts in spelling allows children to keep their self esteem and further their spelling development.

Spelling check-list

Check the children's:
• hearing and vision are within normal range;
• alphabet knowledge: letter names and sounds;
• handwriting: a correctly formed joined up style;
• understanding and recognition of rhyming words;
• strategies for learning spellings, for example Look, Say, Copy, Cover, Write, Check and making analogies with words with common letter patterns.

Page 10: Making small words

This activity sheet provides an opportunity to check the children's knowledge of individual sounds to make consonant–vowel–consonant words. Confirm that all children are familiar with the words 'consonant' and 'vowel' and confident of their use before they begin. Explain that they need to try each vowel sound with the consonants in the rockets to see how many alternative words they can make.
Extension activity: Working in pairs, the children could compare their lists of words and mark the similarities and the differences.

Pages 11–14: Letter strings 1–4

These four activity sheets are based on onset and rime using initial letter sounds and initial blends with common letter strings. The children are required to make analogies with similar sounding words. Use joined up writing for these activities.
Extension activity: Ask the children to choose one of the letter strings from the activity sheet and make up amusing sentences using as many of the words as they can (for example, It was damp in the camp and they needed a lamp.).

Page 15: Tricky words to spell

This sheet will help children who find non-regular key words difficult to spell. Encourage the children to cover their practice attempts as they try the whole word. Emphasise that they must use joined up writing for the letters and the completed word.
Extension activity: Ask the children to each make a list of five or ten words that they themselves find difficult to spell. The children could also work in pairs, writing the problem words for each child on cards laid face down on the table. The children then try to spell their own and each other's words. These will need to be written down and could become a scoring game if the children are keen.

Page 16: Word pairs

A selection of irregular, high frequency words have been chosen for spelling in this activity sheet. The children need to look for similar letter strings and

join them into pairs. Emphasise that the children need to say the words aloud to themselves as this will help them to memorise them for the second activity on the sheet. If necessary, give the children the opportunity to re-check the paired words.
Extension activity: Write the words on individual cards and place them, mixed-up, face down on the table. Let the children take turns to find the pairs as in the game of Pelmanism.

Page 17: Syllables

Before the children attempt this sheet explain syllabification to them practically by clapping out their names, for example. Check that the children understand that the pictures on the activity sheet are there to help them decipher the long words.
Extension activity: Ask the children to think of, or find, words in their books with four syllables in them, and to make a list of these words. Some children will find it helpful if they can tap out the number of syllables.

Grammar

The activity sheets in this section cover a variety of grammatical conventions, including sentence structure, punctuation, nouns, verbs, adjectives and speech marks. They will give the children an opportunity to revisit and reinforce these conventions which are now a requirement within the English National Curriculum. It is important that children understand the structure of written language and can transfer this understanding to their own writing.

Page 18: All about sentences

This activity sheet explains that a sentence is a group of words that make sense. Within the muddled sentences phrases have intentionally been left in to make the task easier. Encourage the children to look for the capital letter to start the sentence and the full stop to end it. In the second activity, lines can be drawn between the first and second part of a sentence to aid the writing out of the sentences. Remind the children to use all the phrases.
Extension activity: Children can work in pairs and write four sentences each on slips of paper. Cut the sentences into two parts and mix them all up together. As a timed activity, how long does it take the children to sort out the sentences? They may find other alternative sentences. Make it fun by using one beginning and two alternative endings – one sense, the other nonsense.

Page 19: Capital letters and full stops

For this activity sheet encourage the children to read the text aloud to themselves, as this will make it easier for them to make sense of the text and note where the full stops should be placed. Initially, let

them use coloured pencils to make the capital letter and full stops on the text, before writing them out under the pictures.
The picture/sentence correspondence is:
1. One day a hare and a tortoise had a race.
2. The hare thought he would win, so he sat down and fell asleep.
3. The tortoise plodded slowly by.
4. He won the race because he didn't give up.
   The correct sentences in the second activity are: The big lion caught a small mouse in its paw; The lion let the mouse go; Some time later the lion was caught in a net; The mouse chewed a hole in the net and let the lion free.
Extension activity: The children can find other Aesop's Fables and draw four pictures from the story, making up four sentences to match.

Page 20: More sentences

Children sometimes find it difficult to begin and end sentences. Encourage them to read the robot story aloud to themselves and then perhaps, to you or a member of the group. Emphasise the need for breath! The children may find it helpful to cross out the 'ands', and to put in capital letters and full stops within the text first, before they rewrite it.
Extension activity: Ask the children to look in their reading books for words and phrases that start a sentence. Make a list of these and let the children compare with each other.

Page 21: All about nouns

Explain to the children that the sentences in this activity sheet have been carefully chosen so that only one noun will fit in each space. Encourage them to tick off each noun in the box as it is used, and then use their chosen nouns in sentences.
Extension activity: Ask the children to choose two pages in their reading book and make a list of all the nouns they can find. Check with a friend or the teacher that the words are correct.

Page 22: Interesting adjectives

As an introduction, ask the children to think of an example from within their own environment, of an object which would be more interesting if an adjective was added to it. For example: A clock (ticking, wooden, large, chiming and so on). Explain to the children that the sentences on the activity sheet, though complete in themselves, would be more exciting if described more fully. First use one adjective in each space, trying each one to make the best selection, then try more than one in each space to add even more interest to each sentence. This leads to a second activity, where other words from the boxes could be used if appropriate.
Extension activity: Choose two pages from a book and make a list of all the adjectives found. Check with a friend that they are correct.

Page 23: All about verbs

Start with a preliminary discussion on verbs which will increase the learning value of this sheet. Explain to the children that the sentences in this activity sheet have been chosen carefully so that only one verb will fit in each space. Tick off each verb in the box as it is used.

Extension activity: The children could make up four sentences with the verbs they have chosen or ask them to choose two pages in their reading book and make a list of all the verbs they can find. They can check with a friend that they are correct.

Page 24: Speech marks

This activity sheet aims to show children the importance of direct speech. Check that they can read the speech within the speech bubbles before they start matching and writing the sentences.

Extension activity: Ask the children to draw their own cartoon picture with direct speech spoken by each of the characters within the picture.

Creative or free writing

These activity sheets introduce the children to different forms of writing including character writing, report writing, story writing, creative writing and writing instructions. All of these formats are now expected at Key Stage 1 and 2, Level 2 and 3 in the National Curriculum.

Writing check-list

- allow time for oral discussion;
- plan or make notes;
- use story prompts;
- joint scribing to help start or complete writing;
- collaborative writing;
- picture stimulus;
- computer for redrafting.

Page 25: Days of the week

This activity sheet will help children who have difficulty in both sequencing and spelling the days of the week. To add another dimension to this activity, the children are asked to use their own ideas for finishing the sentences.

Extension activity: Write the days of the week on separate cards and use as a check for spelling or putting in sequential order.

Page 26: Holiday postcards

Remind the children that what they write must be about the pictures shown on the postcard scenes.

Extension activity: Ask the children to design a postcard of their own. Encourage them to be as creative as possible. Ask for suggestions of unusual holiday locations to give them the opportunity to use their imagination or use pictures from travel brochures as a stimulus.

Page 27: Writing a story

This extends the idea of sequencing story events, but within a limited format which makes the task of writing seem less daunting. Talk to the children about the story to establish some ideas. The alternative endings allow for some decision making.

Extension activity: Can the children think of a title for the story. They can then illustrate it and cut up the story to make it into a book to keep

Page 28: Forest frights

Read and discuss with the children, both the title and the words within the trees. Explain that they do not have to use all the words, and they may also think of alternative words themselves. Emphasise the fact that this is descriptive writing about how they feel and what they would see or hear.

Extension activity: Find a suitable art book, poster or photograph to discuss or write about to extend descriptive writing.

Page 29: Story characters – Jack and the Beanstalk

These have been devised to help children's imaginative writing and allow for an open-ended response. The children may benefit from discussing the characters' feelings in the group, as an introduction to the activity. Use similar activity sheets to encourage inference skills from stories which the children read in class.

Extension activity: Choose a scene from a traditional story and ask the children to draw a picture or cartoon. Let them write about what the characters are thinking or fill in speech bubbles.

Page 30: Writing instructions

Children with literacy difficulties can find writing instructions a difficult task. This activity sheet gives the children an opportunity to study the map and organise the sequence before they start writing. Use a highlighter pen to mark out the route. Remind them that they must name everything they pass.

Extension activity: Ask the children to write from memory their route from home to school. If this is difficult, a route within school could be used.

Page 31: Headlines

Report writing is a specific skill. Let the children practise first on a separate piece of paper. Read examples from the paper to demonstrate this genre.

Extension activity: Ask the children to work out three headlines of their own, on any topic.

Page 32: Riddle game

Make sure that the children understand the concept of a riddle. Provide scissors and glue. Make up other riddles related to your topic work.

Handwriting 1

Tip – Check your pencil grip.

This sheet shows you how patterns help your handwriting.

The ccc pattern family.
● You practise

ccc _____ cccc _____ cc _____ cc _____

ccccc _____ cccc _____ ccc _____ ccc _____

cc _____ cccc _____ ccc _____ cc _____

All these letters are in this family.

a   c   d   e   g   q   o

● You practise

aaa _____ ccc _____ ddd _____ eee _____

ggg _____ qqq _____ ooo _____

● Now try joining some of the letters.

ad _____ _____

ag _____ _____

oc _____ _____

od _____ _____

ca _____ _____

co _____ _____

do _____ _____

● Now try some words.

cat _____ _____

dog _____ _____

cog _____ _____

eat _____ _____

call _____ _____

all _____ _____

dot _____ _____

Handwriting 2

This sheet shows you how patterns help your handwriting.

The ililil pattern family.
● You practise

ilili _____ lili _____ lilili _____ ili _____

ilil _____ ilil _____ ililili _____ ilili _____

lili _____

All these letters are in this family.

↓i   ↓u   ↓y   ↓↓l   ↓t

● You practise

iiii _____ uuu _____ uuuu _____ yyyyy _____

lllll _____ ttt _____

● Now try joining some of the letters.

li _____ _____

ut _____ _____

it _____ _____

ta _____ _____

lu _____ _____

lo _____ _____

ey _____ _____

● Now try some words.

lay _____ _____

till _____ _____

lug _____ _____

tug _____ _____

day _____ _____

tall _____ _____

lot _____ _____

Handwriting 3

This sheet shows you how patterns help your handwriting.

The mm pattern family.
● You practise

mm _____   mm _____   m _____   mm _____

mm _____   mm _____   mmm _____   mm _____

m _____   mm _____   mmm _____   mm _____

All these letters are in this family.

↓r   ↓n   ↓m   ↓h   ↓p   ↓b

● You practise

rrrr _____   nn _____   mmmm _____   hh _____

hh _____   ppp _____   bbb _____

● Now try joining some of the letters.

ni _____ _____

ho _____ _____

op _____ _____

im _____ _____

un _____ _____

na _____ _____

ab _____ _____

● Now try some words.

hop _____ _____

rag _____ _____

man _____ _____

nap _____ _____

mad _____ _____

lob _____ _____

hot _____ _____

● Name _____

Handwriting 4

This sheet shows you how patterns help your handwriting.

Tip –
All letters
except d and e
start at the top
of the letter.

The wwww pattern family.
● You practise

w w w _____ w w w _____ w w _____

w w w _____ w w _____ wwww _____

w w w w w _____

These letters are in this family.
    v   w   x   z

● You practise

v v v v _____ v v v _____ w w w _____ x x x _____

z z z _____ v x z w _____ x z w v _____ z x _____

● Now try joining some of the letters.

wa ____ _____ _____

ze ____ _____ _____

ox ____ _____ _____

va ____ _____ _____

ow ____ _____ _____

zi ____ _____ _____

vi ____ _____ _____

ix ____ _____ _____

● Now try some words.

was ____ _____ _____

van ____ _____ _____

six ____ _____ _____

zigzag ____ _____ _____

vet ____ _____ _____

fox ____ _____ _____

oxo ____ _____ _____

well ____ _____ _____

● ESSENTIALS FOR ENGLISH: Skills for writing   8

Handwriting 5

Tricky letters for you to practise.

f is a tricky letter when it joins up. ● Practise the words.	_fan fed fib fog fan_
r is a tricky letter to join up. It needs an extra dip at the end. r r ● Practise the words.	_ran red rib rob run_
s is a tricky letter to keep the right size. ● Practise the words	_was has this miss bus_
These letters have descenders that go below the line which don't join up. ● Practice the letters and the words.	_g j p q y get jet pin yes_
These letters have ascenders that are tall. ● Practise the letters and the words.	_b f d h k l t back hole dart fall_

● Name _____

Making small words

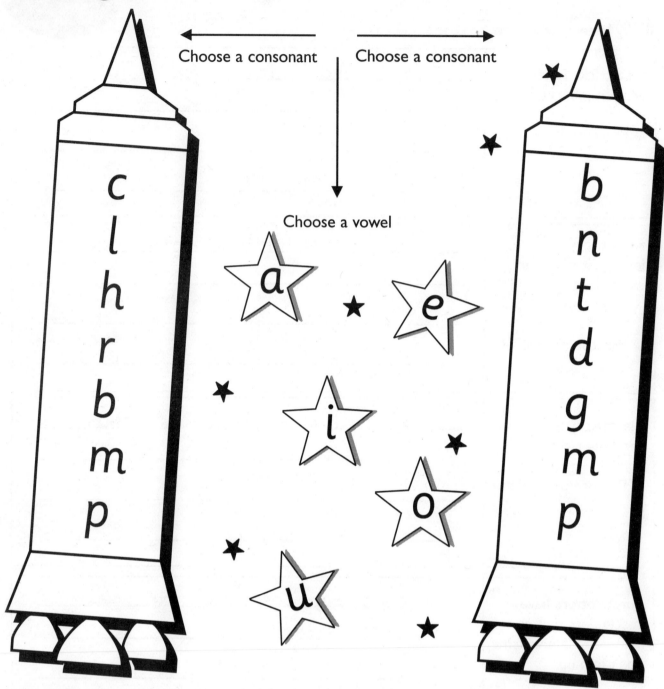

Choose a consonant ← → Choose a consonant

Choose a vowel

● How many words can you make? Write them in the boxes.

a	e	i	o	u
h<u>a</u>m	p<u>e</u>g	b<u>i</u>d	l<u>o</u>p	p<u>u</u>t

● Name _____

Spelling: Letter strings 1

● Take a consonant from the stem of this plant. Using the letter strings on the branches, make a word in each leaf. Use joined up writing.

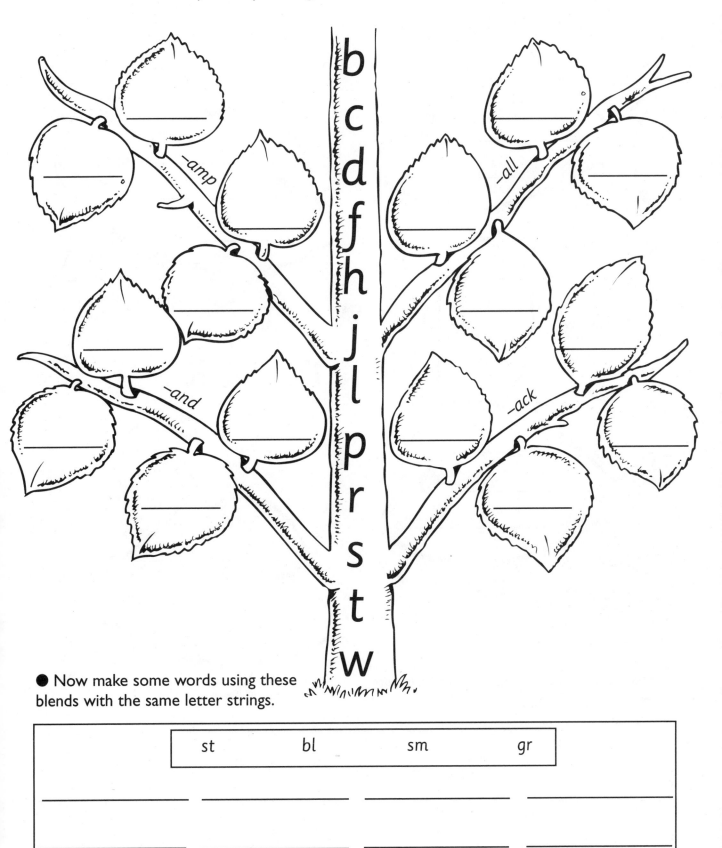

● Now make some words using these blends with the same letter strings.

st	bl	sm	gr

_____   _____   _____

_____   _____   _____

● Name _____

Spelling: Letter strings 2

● Take a consonant from the water. Use the letter strings to make words in each fish. Use joined up writing.

–ish

–ing

–ick

–ill

d   l   b   w   t

f   h   r   k

g   p   s

● Make some words using these blends with the same letter strings.

th	st	ch	qu	sw	br

_____ _____ _____ _____

_____ _____ _____ _____

Spelling: Letter strings 3

● Take a consonant from the body of the moth. Use the letter strings to make words in each wing. Use joined up writing.

-old

_____

_____

_____

-ock

_____

_____

_____

b t
s f c
d l h
w m
r p

-ook

_____

_____

_____

-ound

_____

_____

_____

● Make some words using these blends with the same letter strings.

sh	fr	gr	br	st

_____ _____ _____ _____

_____ _____ _____

Spelling: Letter strings 4

● Take a consonant from the keyboard. Use the letter string on the computer screen to make the words. Write the words on the screen. Use joined up writing.

–ell

_____
_____
_____
_____

b g w k t y

–end

_____
_____
_____
_____

y h l s t b m

–ump

_____
_____
_____
_____

j l t w b h

–ush

_____
_____
_____
_____

d r b n l h

● Make some words using these blends with the same letter strings.

sh	tr	bl	cl	br

_____ _____ _____ _____

_____ _____ _____

● Name _____

Tricky words to spell

● Fill in all the missing letters in the words. Then make a sentence using the three words in each group. Say the letter names as you write them.

said	were	once
sai ___	wer ___	onc ___
sa ___	we ___	on ___
s ___	w ___	o ___
___	___	___

they	know	when
the ___	kno ___	whe ___
th ___	kn ___	wh ___
t ___	k ___	w ___
___	___	___

what	want	with
wha ___	wan ___	wit ___
wh ___	wa ___	wi ___
w ___	w ___	w ___
___	___	___

Three more tricky words.

because	people	friend

● Can you spell them? Cover them up and then try.

● Name _____

Word pairs

● Look for the same letter string. Join the word pairs.
The first pair is done for you.

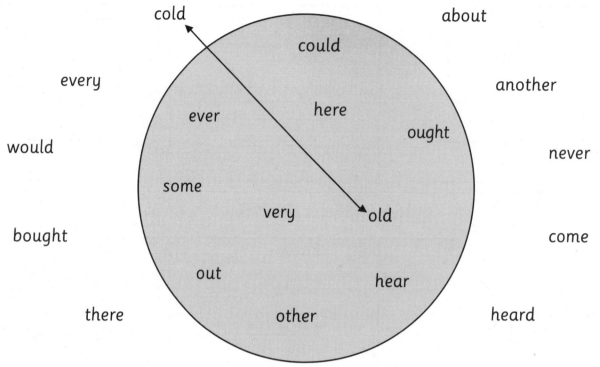

● Cover up the words in this circle with a piece of card. Now see if you can write the matching words below. Use joined up writing.

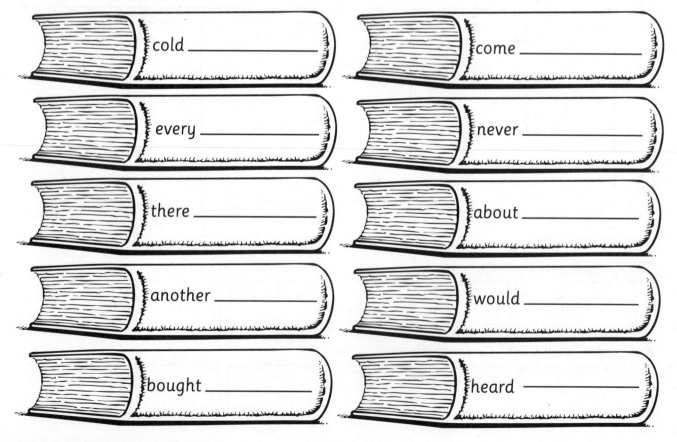

cold _____

come _____

every _____

never _____

there _____

about _____

another _____

would _____

bought _____

heard _____

ESSENTIALS FOR ENGLISH: Skills for writing

Syllables

● Put the syllables in the right order to make a word. Write the whole word on the line and then write the word in a sentence in joined up writing. The first one has been done for you.

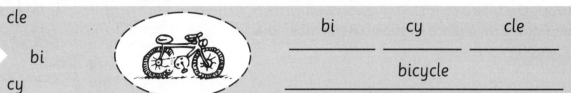

cle

bi

cy

bi	cy	cle

bicycle

I ride my bicycle to school

pu

com

ter

_____ _____ _____

_____

sion

tele

vi

_____ _____ _____

_____

late

choc

o

_____ _____ _____

_____

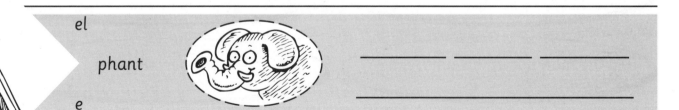

el

phant

e

_____ _____ _____

_____

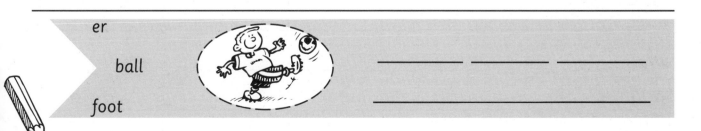

er

ball

foot

_____ _____ _____

_____

All about sentences

A sentence has to make sense. These sentences are in a muddle.

● Turn them into sensible sentences and write them down on a piece of paper. (Remember the full stop!)

1. took The shopping a very long time.

2. to the ground. crashed The tree

3. covered Soon the snow the ground.

4. to school. to take my new book I am going

5. the ice-cream. licked The boy

6. went dancing The girl every week.

● Match the two parts of each sentence and write the complete sentence on the line in joined up writing.

I went into a shop	as it was raining.
For my birthday I had	to buy some chocolate.
In the morning	a surprise present.
The man put up his umbrella	I overslept.

1. _____

2. _____

3. _____

4. _____

● Name _____

Capital letters and full stops

● Read this story.

> ### The Hare and the Tortoise
> One day a hare and a tortoise had a race the hare thought he would win, so he sat down and fell asleep the tortoise plodded slowly by he won the race because he didn't give up

Capital letters and full stops are missing in the story.
● Work out the sentences and write them under the pictures.

1. _____

2. _____

3. _____

4. _____

● Read the story.

> ### The Lion and the Mouse
> A big lion caught a small mouse in its paw the lion let the mouse go some time later the lion was caught in a net the mouse chewed a hole in the net and let the lion free

● Write out the story, putting in the capital letters and full stops.

_____

_____

_____

_____

More sentences

● Read the story all the way through.

A Robot Story

Once upon a time a robot came to stay in our house <u>and</u> when my Mum saw him she was frightened <u>and</u> she wanted him to go away <u>and</u> we asked if he could stay to play with us for a while <u>and</u> Mum thought it would be all right <u>and</u> she said he could stay to tea because she had plenty of fish fingers <u>and</u> we had a really great time playing games with the robot <u>and</u> Dad was really surprised when he came home.

There are a lot of 'ands' underlined in this story.
● Take them out and make the story into sentences with a capital letter at the beginning and a full stop at the end of each one. Write them below.
● Read your story now – it will sound much better!

<u>Once upon a time</u> _____

_____

_____

_____

_____

_____

_____

_____

_____

_____

All about nouns

A noun is a <u>naming</u> word.
Here are some <u>naming</u> words. Can you think of any more? ● Write them in the boxes.

jumper	car	ball	leaves
pizza	arm	chips	monkey

● Choose the correct nouns to finish these sentences.

My favourite food is fish and _____ .

The boy broke his _____ and could not write.

A _____ jumped from tree to tree.

The family went out for the day in the _____ .

We ate a big _____ for lunch.

Grandpa kicked a _____ through the window.

In Autumn _____ fall off the trees.

I left my yellow _____ on the bus.

● Put a circle round any other nouns in these sentences.

● Now make up four sentences with some of these nouns. Write them on the lines below.

1. _____

2. _____

3. _____

4. _____

Interesting adjectives

An adjective is a <u>describing</u> word.
● Choose some adjectives from the boxes to make these sentences more interesting.

A _____ fox sat under a _____ tree.

sly	crafty	beautiful
frightened	red	

huge	small	tall
broken	old	leafy

_____

A _____ boy stood looking at the _____ sea.

small	frightened	strange
tall	thin	

blue	raging	cold
rolling	calm	angry

_____

The _____ cottage was in the _____ wood.

pretty	tumbledown	
white	stone	old

dark	leafy	spooky
gloomy	dense	magic

_____

● Now, make these sentences more interesting by adding some adjectives.

The creature shivered in the ditch.

_____

_____

The children danced to the music.

_____

_____

● Name _____

All about verbs

A verb is an <u>action</u> word.
Here are some <u>action</u> words. Can you think of any more?
● Write them in the boxes.

shout	draw	walk	cry
laugh	climb	sleep	skip

● Choose the correct verb to finish these sentences.

I _____ a picture.

I _____ at a joke.

I _____ at the sad film.

I _____ in a bed.

I _____ up a ladder.

I _____ along the path.

I _____ with a rope.

I _____ at the football match.

● Look at these pictures and write a sentence for each one.
● Put a circle round the verbs you have used.

● You draw a picture and write a sentence.

_____
_____
_____

_____
_____
_____

_____
_____
_____

Speech marks

● Speech marks tell you when someone is talking.
● Match the speech to the right person.

| Be careful when you cross the road. | Time for your injection. | These letters have no post codes. | My trainers are too small. | This spaghetti tastes good. | Quick, quick! The flames are spreading. |

● Now write what each person is saying in the sentences below. Remember to use speech marks. The first one is done for you.

The boy said, "My trainers are too small."

The cook said, _____

The postman said, _____

The nurse said, _____

The policeman said, _____

The fireman said, _____

● Put in the speech marks here:

The juggler grinned at the children, Here you are, you have a go, he said. The children

tried, It's hard, they said. How long did it take you to learn? Ten years or so, he laughed.

● Name _____

Days of the week

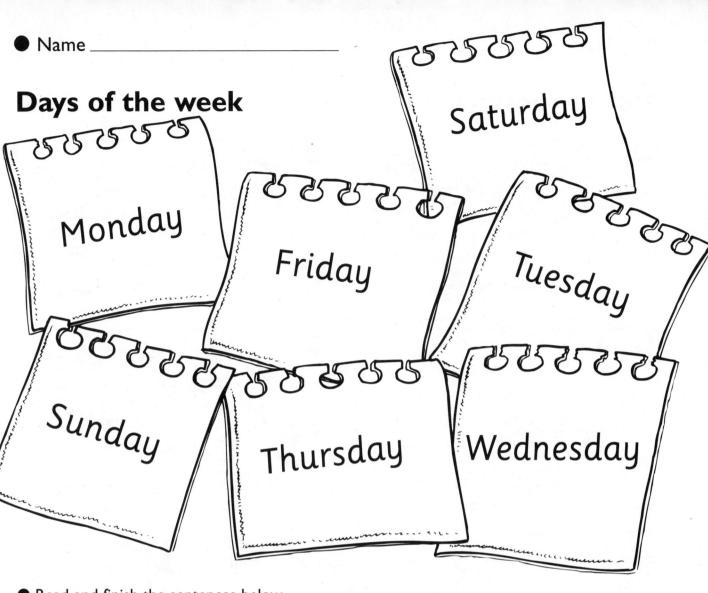

● Read and finish the sentences below.

On M _____ the best thing at school is _____

On T _____ the worst thing at school is _____

On W _____ the most boring thing on television is _____

On Th _____ the nicest thing to do at home is _____

On F _____ the favourite thing for tea is _____

On S _____ the best game to play is _____

On S _____ the most enjoyable time is _____

What I like best is

_____

Holiday postcards

rocks   beach   pool   boat

● Use the words on the shells to complete the sentences.

● Make up another sentence to finish each message.

1. The donkeys were on the _____ again this year.

_____

2. We go swimming in the _____ every day.

_____

3. I nearly fell out of the _____ yesterday.

_____

4. I cut my leg on the _____ .

_____

Writing a story

● Write some more sentences under each of the pictures to make the story more interesting.

Dan looked at the computer screen.

_____

_____

Suddenly the screen lit up.

_____

_____

"Hello" said a funny looking figure,

"I'm Gremlin, who are you?"

_____

_____

Dan gasped in surprise, "Where have

you come from?"

_____

_____

● Choose and write the ending you like best.

← either
or →

_____   _____

_____   _____

_____   _____

_____   _____

● Name _____

Forest frights – creative writing

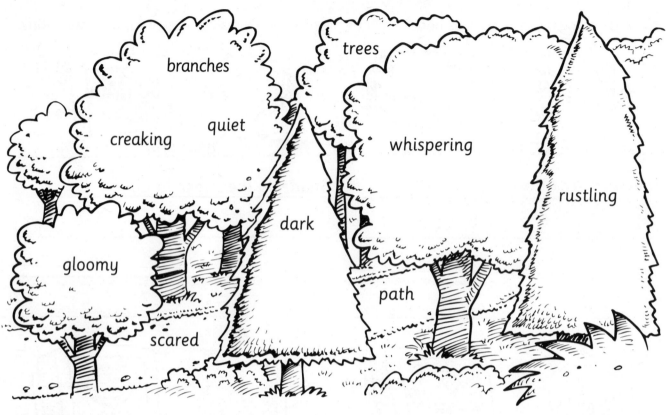

● Write about how it would feel to be lost in a forest. The words in the picture will help you.

_____

_____

_____

_____

_____

_____

_____

_____

_____

_____

_____

Story characters – Jack and the Beanstalk

● What did Jack's mother think when he sold the cow for the beans?

● What did Jack think when he went into the castle?

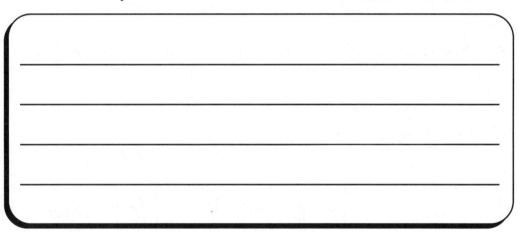

● What did the Giant think when Jack took the gold and ran away?

Writing instructions

Your friend needs to know how to get from Waterland School to the station.
● Work out and write down the instructions.

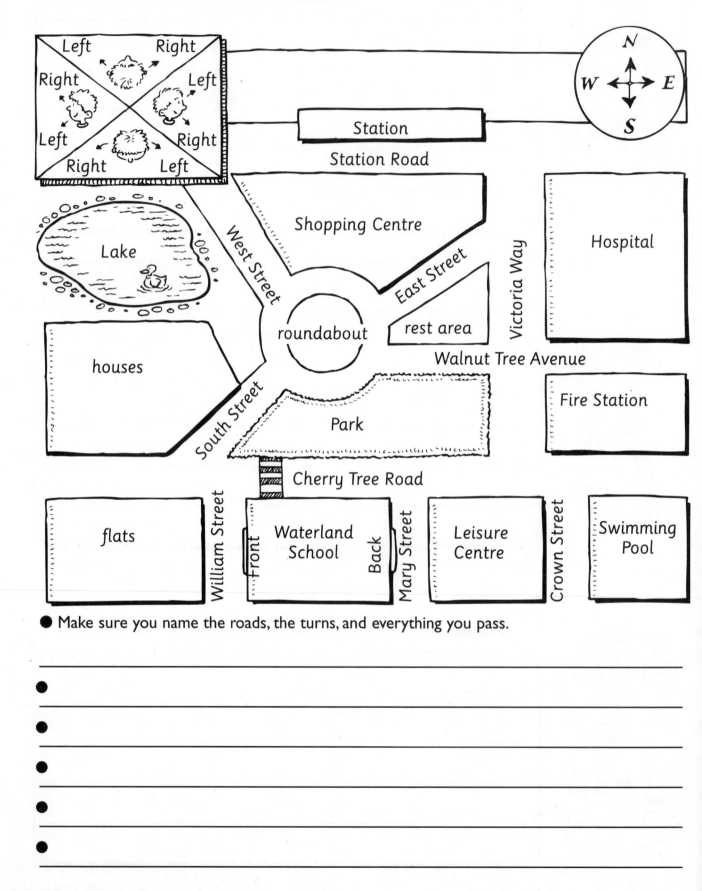

● Make sure you name the roads, the turns, and everything you pass.

● _____
_____
● _____
_____
● _____
_____
● _____
_____
● _____
_____

● Name _____

Headlines

These are headlines from a newspaper. ● Write a report about what happened for each one.

| Man falls in river. Rescued by DOG! |

_____

_____

_____

_____

| Park made safe – bikes banned. |

_____

_____

_____

_____

| FUN for all the family. CIRCUS hits town! |

_____

_____

_____

_____

● Name _____

Riddle game

1. Write down three clues about each picture.
2. Cut out each strip.
3. Fold in half and glue.
4. Place the cards riddle side up on table.

5. Ask a friend to guess the riddles.
6. Check answer with picture.
7. Make up some more.

↓ fold line

● _____
● _____
● _____

↓ fold line

● _____
● _____
● _____

↓ fold line

● _____
● _____
● _____

↓ fold line

● _____
● _____
● _____